C000259541

Bumblebees

Dr. John Feltwell, F.R.E.S., F.L.S.

Wildlife Matters

Published by Wildlife Matters
Marlham, Henley's Down, Battle, East Sussex, TN33 9BN, UK

Also published by Wildlife Matters
The Conservation of Butterflies in Britain, past and present

Some other books by John Feltwell
Animals and Where They Live (Dorling Kindersley)
Butterflies and Moths (Dorling Kindersley)
Butterflies & Other Insects of Britain (Reader's Digest)
Butterflies of North America (Dragon's World)
Countryside Conservation (Ebury Press)
Discovering Doorstep Wildlife (Hamlyn)
Encyclopedia of Butterflies of the World (Quarto)
Meadows - A History and Natural History (Alan Sutton)
The Natural History of Butterflies (Croom Helm)
The Story of Silk (Alan Sutton)
Clematis for all Seasons (Collins & Brown)

This publication may not be reproduced, scanned, stored or transmitted electronically, in any form or by any means, without the prior permission in writing of the publishers. This does not affect the provisions laid out in the UK Copyright Designs and Patents Act, 1988 regarding fair dealing for the purposes of research or private study, or criticism or review.

First published 2006
ISBN 0-907970-03-6 ISBN 978-0-907970-03-3
© 2006 John Feltwell / Wildlife Matters.
The author asserts his rights over the text and all colour photographs.
The bumblebee line drawing © Brian Hargreaves

4 BUMBLEBEES

Contents

Introduction

Bumblebees have too few friends.There has been a noticeable decline in bumblebee numbers in the countryside and habitat loss is their enemy. This book seeks to give bumblebees a much higher profile, and to promote a greater awareness for these loveable creatures.

Bumblebees, or humble bees as Charles Darwin talked of them, are certainly busy bees. Their industriousness and diligence in seeking out nectar and pollen in the garden, along the wayside and woodland has to be admired.

Many people are scared of bumblebees though they have no reason to be. They do have stings but hardly ever use them. The fact that they are quite big and dark and look scary perhaps does the trick. A big black beast slowly cruising around is all that is needed to warn predators – even humans.

In fact bumblebees are one of the most easy going members of the wasps and bees group and are generally not inclined to sting anyone. They go on their way around our gardens, doing good, pollinating wildflowers, in the copse or woodland, enjoying the rows of peas and beans in the kitchen garden, on the allotment. If you do not disturb them, they will not disturb you.

Bumblebees are beautiful too. They have bright colour bands of yellow, orange, white contrasted against black, or brown. They are harder workers than honeybees and are out earlier in the morning and later in the day. If you are outdoors in the evening badger watching, the only things that move in the woods are small mammals and bumblebees working at dusk.

So bumblebees are part of our northern temperate countryside, and quite at home in the flowering meadows, along hedgerows, riverbanks and in our gardens, in fact anywhere that wildflowers provide feeding stations.They are perfectly acclimatised to the vagaries of weather, and cope with April showers, torrential autumn rain, and periods of unexpectedly cool weather. And they are coping with global warming.

They are attuned to flowers that give them food, and include a wide variety of colourful wild and garden flowers amongst their sources. Having either short or long tongues has allowed them to exploit a wide range of flora, but this may have played against those with long tongues since some of the wildflowers with long flower tubes are disappearing. This is where gardens can provide the flowers that the countryside now lacks.

The whole reason for writing this book has been simply to share the enjoyment of studying bumblebees for what they are. This has been done through the 150 colour photographs and factual information supplied. It is not intended to be a definitive guide to bumblebees or an identification book, just a means to stimulate others to take up the bumblebee baton, to find out more, so that we are all in a better position to conserve them in their uncertain future.

Ragwort, *Senecio jacobaea*, is an important nectar source for bumblebees

The Bumblebee as a gentle giant

It's big, black and hairy but it's not a brute. It's a bluffer.
The bumblebee has all the appearance of being a formidable insect, but in fact it is very docile and loveable and hardly does anyone harm. Its deception or *modus operandi* gives the impression of being a brute and it flies deliberately and slowly so that everyone gets the message.

The bumblebee is an insect that has three pairs of legs, two pairs of wings (one large, the other small) and one pair each of antennae (feelers) and compound eyes. The eyes are called compound since each 'eye' is made up of many tiny lenses. The body of all bumblebees is made of three parts, head, thorax (the middle section) and the abdomen. The wings and legs are attached to the thorax that contains inside the powerful muscles that power the wings. The abdomen contains the reproductive organs, especially the genitalia at the end (not often seen) and the sting. Like any other insect, bumblebees are segmented and this can be seen easily in the thorax and abdomen. The body is covered by hairs which wear off over time, and the colours of hairs that are present on different segments is helpful in their identification.

Only queens and worker bumblebees have a sting; males (drones) have none
Only males have seven segments in their abdomens; females have six
Only queens have a pollen basket

Characteristics

The presence or absence of facial hair is an important identification feature of bumblebees. This one has yellow facial hair that helps to identify it as the Early Bumblebee, *Bombus pratorum*. The colour of the bands of hairs are also very useful in identification, but they can fade with time, creating a very light banded bumblebee. Conversely dark forms of bumblebees may be seen, and all this colour variation hinders identification. The yellow and black colour scheme is a warning to predators to stay away. In these specimens some of the characteristics of the insect can be seen: the compound eyes, the jointed antennae (above), and the three pairs of legs (in the lower one).

Bumblebees have either short, mid or long tongues, that makes a big difference which flowers they can visit, or rob

The Bee sung by Mr. Raworth at Marylebone Gardens

This eighteenth century song eloquently captures some of the behaviour of bumblebees in town and country, the plants and habitats it visits. (*Royal Magazine*, Volume 16, 1767. p. 45).

Marylebone is in North London and had extensive gardens with concert halls and spas. The gardens were built over 1778 to make way for the growth of London. This song therefore epitomises the problem for bumblebees - where once they were common, now they are gone.

A buffy humble bee am I,
that ranges the garden sunny,
From flow'r to flow'r I changing fly,
And ev,,,ry flow'r 's my honey,
Bright Chlo..e with her golden hair,
A while my rich jonquils,
Till cloy'd with siping Nectar there,
I shift to rosy Phillis I shift,
I shift to ro..sy Phillis, Phillis, I shift to ro...sy Phillis.

But Phillis's sweet opening breath,
Remains not long my station,
For Kitts must be now addreft,
My spicy-breath'd carnation;
Yet Kitty's fragrant bed, I leave,
To others flow'rs I'm rover,
And all in turns my love receives,
The gay wide garden over,
The gay, &c.

Variety that know no bounds,
my roving fancy edges,
And off with Flora I am found,
In dalliance under hedges,
For I am an errant bee,
Who range each bank that's sunny,
Both fields and gardens are my see,
And every flow'rs my honey
And ev...ry...

What you can do

- Look out for bumblebee nests in the garden. Bumblebees do not come and go so often as honeybees, as they have very small colonies. Look out for a single bumblebee entering a hole in the ground, or check a bird nest box to see whether it has been taken over by bumblebees.

Life Cycle

A large queen is in charge of this thriving colony of *Bombus lapidarius*, the Red-tailed Bumblebee.

A worker of *Bombus pascuorum,* the Common Carder-bee tends the larvae in the nest.

Just like honeybees, bumblebees build wax cells in which to rear their young. The large females straddle the closed cells and incubate the larvae. Honey-pots full of rich nectar supply food for the modest colony.

Bumblebees have three forms, queens, workers and males (drones). Only the mated queen hibernates during winter, the rest dying off. In the spring the queen finds a suitable place to make a nest, often underground, perhaps in an old mouse nest. Here she lays eggs, fertilising them as she goes. She shows a lot of parental care, incubating the developing larvae inside the wax cells she has made (as seen above). The colony grows to about 200 individuals, and they spend the spring, summer and autumn foraging for pollen and nectar. The workers do most of the foraging, generally around 400 metres from the nest. Note the 'honey-pots' in the photograph above, this is concentrated nectar which is used as a food source. Later in the year males emerge and these mate with fresh queens. Queens mate in late autumn and then find a different place in which to hibernate underground, perhaps in some wood debris, a crack in the soil or in a pile of leaves.

- *It takes 3-6 weeks from egg to adult, in spring, in one generation, sometimes two in warm autumns and mild winters.*
- *There are 100-400 bumblebees in a colony, depending on species (compared to honeybees with up to 60,000 in high summer.)*

Bumblebee look-alikes

There are lots of other insects that look like bumblebees and amongst them are other bees, such as honeybees and solitary bees, true flies and some day-flying moths. They have all taken on the disguise of bumblebees and try to pass themselves off as something not worth eating with a sting in its tail. The nature of the disguise is to simulate the size, colour, flight pattern and sound of the bumblebee, so as to confuse predators such as birds, lizards and some mammals. In reality there is overall confusion fostered amongst predators since there are so many insects that have employed the same sort of colour scheme. This shared phenomenon is called Müllerian mimicry (named after the behavioural scientist Mr. Müller) and is a useful ploy used by many animals in the living world. There is some overlap between bees and wasps, with a yellow and black banding typical of wasps and a more subdued brown, black and yellow found in bees and bumblebees.

Other bees (Honeybees, Solitary bees and Carpenter bees)

One of the most frequently encountered bees is the honeybee since it will be foraging at many of the same flowers as the bumblebee. It is more uniform in colour with no yellow and white bands, and could possibly be confused with a worn *B. pascuorum* or a *B. sylvarum*. There are over 200 solitary bee species in Britain and many of them are small and light brown and some make bumblebee buzzing sounds so they do look more like honeybees. One of the largest European carpenter bees is now found in Britain.

True Flies

Some of the relatives of the housefly also look and sound like bumblebees. They all belong to the order of insects called Diptera, and amongst these the hoverflies or syrphids have evolved the most mimicry of bumblebees. Hoverflies mimic both bees and bumblebees as well as wasps in both size and behaviour and are easily confused. Amongst the true flies are the bee flies that seem to hover in front of flowers and probe for nectar using their long thin tongues. Some of the horse-flies can look a little bee like and will rest on vegetation like bumblebees.

Moths

Hovering in front of flowers is typical of the humming-bird hawk moth which is unusual amongst moths, being active in the day. There are two other day-flying relatives, the Broad-bordered and Narrow-bordered Bee hawk moths. Differences with bumblebees include a very long tongue, longer wings and an ability to hover.

What you can do

- Double check the bumblebees in the garden and wayside and check for mimics.
- Look, listen and carefully inspect all the insect features.

Bumblebee look-alikes

There are many insects such as true flies and other bees that look like bumblebees in size, colour and hairiness, and some that have the same buzzing sound. They have evolved this strategy to confuse and deter predators.

A familiar insect, the honey bee, *Apis mellifera,* has a much longer body, and a shorter working day than bumblebees, yet it still works the same flowers.

Another bumblebee mimic and hoverfly, *Merodon equestris* (above left) has the customary deep pile of hairs on its body like bumblebees, large compound eyes and transparent wings. It is fairly common and very variable with a number of colour forms.

Only one insect on this page has a sting

Look-alikes

Bee-flies are often mistaken for bumblebees since they are small, have long tongues and are the same size. They are in fact true flies and belong to the Diptera order of insects. This one is a *Bombylius* sp, nectaring on Red Valerian, *Centranthus ruber.* Two British bee-flies are Biodiversity Action Plan (BAP) species.

One of the largest bee-flies, this one called *Villa* has characteristically long wings. There are a small number of species of *Villa* in Britain, one of which is extinct. All bee-flies are true flies (Order Diptera). It is a very flighty insect but will eventually settle so it can be studied at close quarters.

With very distinctive delta-shaped wings and bold black and white markings, this is a Horse-fly or tabanid. (*Chrysops relictus*, Order Diptera). Female tabanids attack mammals including man and suck blood. They are often found resting on vegetation close to water. Note the shiny green compound eyes.

These wasp-like features of yellow and black markings are typical of many species of hoverfly, this one is *Syrphus* species (Order Diptera). The colours help to confuse predators so that they cannot tell the difference between wasps, bees, and bumblebees – so the edible one has a chance to get away.

Buzzing and flying like a bumblebee, this Leaf-cutting bee or *Megachile* sp, visits a French marigold (*Tagetes patula*) to collect pollen - only females do this. It is the same order as bumblebees (Hymenoptera) but it is in a separate group of solitary bees. Some similar bees are covered in yellow or orange with pollen.

Variation in colour and pattern is typical in insects and this frustrates identification. This is a *Zonaria* sp. hoverfly with attractive maroon and yellow orange markings, here feeding on nectar from a French Marigold (*Tagetes patula*). The maroon markings on the thorax make it very distinctive. It is found in the UK and on the Continent.

As true-flies go, this one looks menacing with its darkly pronounced compound eyes, long legs and back hairs on its body. It is called in latin *Eustalomyia festica*, and breeds in the bodies of flies that have been stashed by solitary wasps. Here it is resting on French Marigold (*Tagetes patula).*

A hoverfly (*Volucella pellucens*) rests on *Buddleia*; the larvae live in wasp nests and eat wasp larvae. The adult fly has a black thorax and black base of its abdomen, but a white band at the base of the abdomen. This hoverfly is about the same size as a bumblebee and could easily be confused for one.

Look-alikes

Bumblebees have to co-exist in a world of clever deception

Bumblebee Mimics

Of all the bumblebees likely to be seen in the garden, this is the commonest. It is known as the Common Carder-bee *Bombus pascuorum*, and may be seen from spring to late autumn. This is a fresh specimen, with good colour, but they can look very scraggy and dull. Usually they are busy foraging; this one is resting.

A brown bumblebee mimic, the hoverfly species, *Criorhina* sp. It is very distinctive and territorial, looking out for female bumblebees, and attacking, even head-butting females, mates and competitors. Usually found in the late spring in southern England it is a bumblebee mimic of *Bombus pascuorum*.

The characteristic red abdomen, with at least the three quarters of the abdomen covered in red, identifies this unique species called the Mountain Humblebee, *Bombus monticola*. It is now found in Wales having disappeared from the more elevated areas of ground (eg. heathlands) in south east England.

Looking like a bumblebee, this is the solitary bee *Osmia bicolor*, that is also a Mason bee - because they often make nests in brickwork. It is here feeding on Rosemary, *Rosmarinus officinalis*. The distinguishing features of this bumblebee look-alike are the long antennae and the abdomen covered in so much red.

The Red-tailed bumblebee, *B. lapidarius* typically has a red tail as its name suggests. Here it is busily taking nectar from a Common Knapweed flower, *Centaurea nigra*.

A cuckoo, the Hill Cuckoo bee, *Bombus rupestris* feeding on Common knapweed, *Centaurea nigra,* has some of its orange hairs faded to white.

Cuckoos

Cuckoo bumblebees are imposters that are the same size and colour as bumblebees, and which gain access to colonies and use the host bumblebee to raise its larvae. There are specific cuckoos for specific species of bumblebee, and one of the ways of telling them apart is that female cuckoos do not have pollen baskets. All cuckoos used to be called *Psithyrus*, now they are all *Bombus*.

Bumblebee Mimics

True

Mimic

True

Mimic

True

Cuckoo

Birds are the predators that have stimulated this evolution by natural selection

Gardening for bumblebees – early spring

Bombus pascuorum, the Common Carder bee, working the nectar from the white flowers of *Pieris japonica*, the Lily of the Valley Bush, or shrub - a very valuable addition to the wildlife garden. Its little flowers like heather bells have plenty of nectar. This large shrub carries lots of flowers for a long time in the spring and is a worthwhile nectar source for bumblebees

Bombus sp. bumblebee taking nectar from the individual flowers of Grape Hyacinth, *Muscari*. Grown from bulbs planted in the late winter, these plants can be grown in windowboxes so that the insects they attract can be seen at very close quarters. It is a pleasure to watch bumblebees coming to visit the petite flowers of Grape Hyacinth and work so hard imbibing nectar.

A female *Bombus lucorum*, the White-tailed Bumblebee, prepares to fly up into the open flower of Snakes' Head Fritillary, *Fritillaria meleagris*. They visit to collect pollen, and then pop out just as fast as they arrive. The three pairs of legs can easily be seen. After the queens emerge from hibernation they can be seen exploring new nectar sources as they become available

One of the commonest bumblebees, the Red-tailed Bumblebee, *Bombus lapidarius*, feeds on nectar from Oregon Grape, *Mahonia* x *media*. This is a large female. Mahonia are bushy and spiky shrubs but good value for bumblebees all year. The yellow flowers are a magnet for bumblebees from spring to autumn.

What you can do

- Look out for the large female bumblebees in the garden, and in municipal gardens on the warmest days of the year. Note how they are searching for nesting spots and nectar sources.
- Find a good nectaring station and wait for bumblebees to arrive.
- Plant spring bulbs such as *Muscari, Fritillaria, Ornithogalum* and *Crocus*, to attract bumblebees.

Pieris is an excellent nectar source

Grape hyacinths (*Muscari* sp.) are very attractive to bumblebees over a long period in the spring. Some varieties give more nectar than others.

The evergreen foliage plant, Oregon Grape (*Mahonia* sp.) is a place where bumblebees gather to drink nectar.

Bumblebees work much longer hours than honeybees

Spring flowers

April showers catch bees unawares on flowers and they have sit it out and wait until the sun dries them. Their plentiful hairs help to insulate them from heat loss. Here a Buff-tailed bumblebee, *Bombus terrestris*, looks bedraggled on rhododendron flowers. Its hairs are all stuck together but the sunshine will dry them out and it will be airborne soon.

Bumblebees do not come prettier than this queen *Bombus pratorum*, the Early Bumblebee with its livery of orange black and yellow. Here it is on the colourful bracts of *Clematis montana "Odorata"*, the subtly-scented and floriferous clematis worthy of any garden. Clematis flowers, like roses, are not high on the list of flowers visited by bumblebees.

The Early Bumblebee, *Bombus pratorum*, feeding on the Macedonian scabious, *Knautia macedonica* 'Melton Pastels' is especially attractive to bumblebees for its nectar. Bumblebees will travel far to work the mass of flowers. All the scabious species are useful to bumblebees and they can be grown as hardy perennials in wild or cottage gardens. They have a fairly long flowering period, especially if dead-headed.

Tall flowering stems of *Salvia verticillata* 'Purple Rain' – an herbaceous perennial – have whorls of flowers that bring in bumblebees as one of their favoured nectar sources. The plant makes a good focus for bumblebees with its tall spreading stems bearing large quantities of flowers. Here a queen Garden Bumblebee, *Bombus hortorum*, is busing working the flowers.

The Red-tailed Bumblebee, *Bombus lapidarius* is as big as the yellow flower of Spring Cinquefoil, *Potentilla tabernaemontani*, which it is eager to relieve of its pollen; note the pollen load on its hind leg - therefore this one has to be a queen. Spring Cinquefoil occurs naturally on dry short-turfed areas along paths, verges and wasteland.

What you can do

- Look out for Spring Cinquefoil on dry wasteland or beside paths, and you should then find bumblebees.

Worker bumblebees carry about 259 microlitres of nectar in their stomachs (a microlitre is a millionth of a litre – i.e. very small)

Spring queens in the border

*Heavy queens can
weigh up to 0.85 grams*

Wildflower gardening

What you can do for bumblebees

Gardens have plenty to offer for bumblebees even the tiniest of gardens, patios or windowboxes can provide nectar and pollen sources. All the bumblebees shown on the opposite page were photographed in the wild, on hawkweed, ragworts, mignonette, black horehound, clover, bramble and spring cinquefoil. But the list could go on to include Borage, *Borago officinalis*, Common fleabane, *Pulcicaria dysenterica,* or White deadnettle, *Lamium alba*.

Getting started

You do not always need to plant wildflowers, since if you leave a little patch of ground to go wild then the local wildflowers may well colonise all by themselves. You may live next to a brownfield site or bit of wasteland in which case look out for patches of suitable wildflowers. If you are going to grow your own wildflowers then try to go for native instead of introduced species, since they are likely to have a better chance of attracting bumblebees.

If you want to make a wildflower meadow that will attract all sorts of insects including bumblebees then a tip is to use a part of the garden that is not rich in nutrients. Wildflowers do best where the soil is sparse and is not pampered with fertilisers and enriched with compost. You will need to buy a wildflower mix from one of the suppliers (listed at the end of the book).

Preparing the ground first is the key to success. Invasive weeds need to be removed then the soil raked over to make it finer. If it is too heavy with clay then lighten it with some sand. The soil needs to be well drained. Sow the seed early to mid spring to get results in summer and autumn, or plant in autumn to have a late spring meadow.

Patios, walls and trellises

Many people only have a tiny garden, but there is still plenty to do to have the pleasure of bumblebees visiting. Pots on patios can be planted up with Scabious, either Field Scabious, *Knautia arvensis*, or Devil's bit scabious, *Succisa pratensis* or Cornflower, *Centaurea cyanus*, or Sea Holly, *Eryngium maritimum*. You can buy potted foxgloves in garden centres, and these can just be put into bigger pots on the patio as they grow. Native climbers for a patio wall or trelliswork would include Clematis and Jasmine.

Windowboxes

Windowboxes are best planted up with wildflowers that are tall and flower for a long time and can readily be seen and enjoyed from inside the house. Top of the list might be chives, *Allium schoenoprasum*, or Betony, *Betonica officinalis,* or Yellow archangel, *Lamiastrum galeobdolon* , or if you can get away with it knapweeds and thistles.

All these wildflowers are good for bumblebees

The Mountain Humble-bee, *Bombus monticola* on a yellow Hawk-weed, *Hieraceum* sp. (left) The Buff-tailed bumblebee *Bombus terrestris*, nectaring on Ragwort (*Senecio jacobaea*) (right) Note how its hair perfectly colour-matches the ragwort florets (right)

Mignonette (left), Clover (above) and Black Horehound (Right) offer suitable nectar sources.

A bumblebee takes nectar from bramble (*Rubus* sp.) (left) and pollen from Spring Cinquefoil (*Potentilla* sp.) (right) both good feeding stations in warm summer weather.

Bumblebees take their cue from where others are feeding and then go there

Wildflower gardening:
Foxgloves and bumblebees

Foxgloves and bumblebees are made for each other. Neither could survive without the other; the flower gets pollinated; the bumblebee gets its nectar. It's a perfect example of evolution between two completely different species where each partner benefits from the association. Bumblebees and foxgloves have been in this relationship since before man was on earth, time enough to make the association near perfect and highly specialised. We are just spectators in this natural evolutionary process; here are some of the specialisms.

The foxglove flowers are perfectly formed to invite and encourage the bumblebee to enter. The bright purple flowers probably help the bumblebee to see the plant from not too far. Then there is a special landing-stage for the bumblebee and the spots are important too. They help the insect to locate the exact entry position by reflecting ultra-violet light that we cannot see into visual guides for the bumblebee.

The flower is also perfectly formed for access for bumblebees since it is tubular and just fits the portly body of the bumblebee. When the bumblebee enters the tube it trundles upwards along the tubular flower to the nectaries situated at the base of the flower - a favourite trick of plants having the nectaries tucked away in a difficult place - ensuring that insects have to brush past the sexual parts of the flowers, the anthers and stigma. By doing this they collect pollen on their body hair that is deposited on the stigmas of the next foxglove flowers they enter. If they have pollen on them from a previous foxglove it may be deposited now. This cross pollination results in fertilisation and breeding success for the foxglove. The bumblebee is an unwitting player of pollination and gets a reward.

Bumblebees are extremely well endowed with body hair, and for good reason. The hairs on a bumblebees body have a dual function, not only collecting and depositing pollen, but insulating the bumblebee, conserving energy, stabilising and maintaining its body temperature. If they did not have the dense pile of hair they would not be able to regulate themselves for flight in cool weather and to keep their temperature up - not bad for a 'cold-blooded' animal.

There are about fifteen species of foxgloves to choose from for the garden, but the best is the Common Foxglove, *Digitalis purpurea* with its dark purple flowers. Occasionally white or spotted foxgloves appear and these are just as good for bumblebees. Foxgloves are either biennial or perennial but are always good value in the garden, even if a big clump takes up a lot of space.

What you can do

- Grow foxgloves in the garden, but remember they flower in their second year. Wait by the foxglove flowers and hopefully a bumblebee will visit soon.
- Go for a walk and find out where your nearest bank of foxgloves is, then you can monitor them daily or weekly for bumblebees. Can you distinguish the different species that make visits?

Bumblebees keep their internal body temperature at 30-40°C during flight

Bumblebees beat their wings up to 200 times per second

In the woods

Encouraging biodiversity is more than just bumblebees. Here in a late 19th century print from *Science for All* (c. 1890) by Robert Brown FLS, are bumblebees visiting violets, and a privet hawk-moth feeding on cowslip flowers. It is said that violets are dependent upon insects for this pollination.

What you can do

Check your beans: as Charles Darwin noted: ...when the Humble-bees bite holes at the base of the flower...'hardly a bean will set'. In today's world, with the paucity of bumblebees, you may be lucky indeed to get any pollinators in the kitchen garden.

Look out for bumblebees in woods, especially bluebell woods

In the Kitchen Garden

Kiwi flower with *B. terrestris*

French bean with *B. pascuorum*

Peach flower with *B. pratorum*

Tomato with *B.terrestris*

Bumblebees are usually faithful to one sort of flower, except late in the season when time and weather are against them. Collecting a mixed load of pollen from two sources makes for economy (right). Here a queen Buff-tailed Bumblebee, *B. terrestris* forages on a cultivated blackberry, *Rubus* sp. Bumblebees are fond of the flowers of soft fruits, and they will also visit peach and kiwi flowers trained against a wall on a trellis.

Bumblebees usually forage at one type of flower during the day, but they choose different flowers through the season.

A very fresh Early Bumblebee, *Bombus pratorum* worker in full colours sips nectar from a *Geranium macrorrhizum* flower. The plant is easy to grow and drought tolerant and produces plenty of flowers.

Catmint, *Nepeta cataria*, provides *Bombus pascuorum, the Common* Carder – Bee, nectar from its long tubular flowers. This is a herbaceous perennial that is useful for bumblebees for its long flowering period.

A queen Buff-tailed Bumblebee, *Bombus terrestris* rests for a moment with its forelegs in the air, having visited a flower of Snapdragon, *Anthirrhinum*.

A queen of the Early Bumblebee, *Bombus pratorum* visits *Buddleia x weyeriana* 'Golden Glow' – a useful though straggly shrub that flowers for a long time.

Dusted in pollen, this queen Early Bumblebee, *Bombus pratorum* is taking nectar from Macedonian Scabious, *Knautia macedonica* 'Melton Pastels'

With tongue extended a female Buff-tailed bumblebee, *Bombus terrestris* prepares to enter a Nasturtium flower, *Tropaeolum major*, the flowers of which run well into early winter.

Geraniums are generally good for bumblebees that take their nectar - Geranium species and their varieties, such as this one *G. ibericum* rather than pelargoniums (commonly called geraniums that are not that good for attracting bumblebees).

A Common Carder Bizzie Lizzie, or Bee, *Bombus pascuorum,* takes a break from visiting the flowers of *Impatiens* growing on the riverbank. This is Britain's commonest bumblebee species.

Bumblebees have been found alive impaled on thorns - a larder for some birds

Gardening for bumblebees -
Early Summer

Most bumblebees in Britain are also found on the Continent

Biodiversity

Gardening for bumblebees
High Summer

Herbaceous borders in mid to late summer are often buzzing with bumblebees. Lavenders (opposite top left) are always a reliable source of nectar as are salvias particularly *Salvia verticillata* 'Purple Rain' (top, middle). If the flower tube is too long as in the large blue salvia, *Salvia patens* 'Guanajuato' (bottom, middle) then the bumblebee robs the flower using its mandibles to bite through the petals. Salvias are all good nectar sources for insects and bumblebees and are worth exploring, since they come in many different colours and heights and they are generally good at growing in hot dry conditions. They occur naturally in central and South America and so are used to drought conditions. A tall shrub called the Chaste Bush (*Vitex agnus-castus)* is worth getting since it continues to flower beyond late summer. It has long plumes of flowers that are attractive to bumblebees. The Globe Thistle, *Echinops* sp. has large round heads of flowers and bumblebees gather on the surface to probe the flowers for nectar. There are a number of useful echinops species, some growing low, some growing tall and majestic, but all used to poor soils and drought tolerant. Some like *E. ritro* grow on limestone areas on the Continent and can survive blazing hot summers with hardly any rainfall and the bumblebees love them. Another perennial for the flower border would include tall veronicas with their blue flowers, and Monkshood or Wolf's Bane, *Aconitum napellus*. It flowers during the summer and then again in autumn. It is interesting to watch bumblebees on monkshood as they land on a "landing stage' - a lower petal which then gives them access to the nectaries which they reach underneath the 'hood' formed by the upper petals. The bumblebee is then in an excellent position to brush by the pollen and thus start the pollination process.

Robbing

If you watch bumblebees working flowers you will notice eventually that some do not take the nectar by the conventional route, i.e. by the open front of the flower, but they go round the back and find the nectaries that way. This is called robbing, because it denies the flower the possibility of being pollinated. Those flowers that have long flower tubes (called corolla tubes) present some difficulties for bumblebees, as different species have different tongue lengths. In foxglove the tube is large enough for entry of the whole bumblebee and there is no need to rob. But those bumblebees that can't reach the nectaries in the conventional way find another way in, maybe probing the tongue between two petals or cutting a hole through with their pair of jaws. Certain flowers such as Comfey, *Symphytum officinale*, or bluebell. are robbed all the time, Petunias and salvias are often robbed too. Finding the quick way to the nectar is good for the bumblebee but at the expense of the flower.

What you can do

- Plant a flower border with drought-tolerant perennials
- Check out flowers that are robbed and see if they set seed.

Blue and purple flowers are particularly attractive to bumblebees

Good Nectar Sources

Though commonly known as The Butterfly Bush, buddleias (*B. davidii*) are excellent for bumblebees. They attract a host of insects to their long colourful spikes and rich scent. Bumblebees go more for colour than scent, but the very first buddleia to come out in the spring is the non-typical buddleia, an evergreen species buddleia called *B. globosa*. Bumblebees love the little orange balls of tiny flowers and avidly probe these for nectar. Another good nectar source is zinkia, shown opposite (bottom).

Did you know - poisonous nectar

Bumblebees sometimes die from taking nectar. The phenomenon is widespread and is believed to be caused by poisonous nectar. Lime flowers and rhododendron flowers are the main culprits producing nectar that in some cases stupefies bumblebees that fall to the ground, crawl around, then die. The bumblebees shown below were collected under lime trees in a town centre during July. They are all queens, and all had their stings protruding (though not seen in the photo below). It is thought that this poisonous nectar puts the bumblebees at risk to predation when they can only crawl. In some cases, but not in this one, the bodies may have holes made by the beaks of birds that are after the honey load carried in their bodies. Quite why some nectars are apparently poisonous is not understood since it would seem to defeat the object of the insect-plant association with regards to rewards for the insect and getting pollination done.

A queen bumblebee can live for up to 9 months including hibernation

The Orange Ball Tree, *Buddleia globosa* is the first buddleia to flower each year and provides bumblebees with plenty of nectar. It differs from other buddleias as it flowers on last years growth only, so it is important to prune this species immediately after flowering and not in the spring before it flowers. It has the advantage of being frost hardy too.

Wildflowers and Garden flowers for bumblebees

N = Native wildflower to Britain   Med = Mediterranean native

Aconitum napellus Monkshood	N
Actinidia chinensis Kiwi	
Agrimonia eupatorium Common Agrimony	N
Allium schoenoprasum Chive	N
Anthirrhinum sp. Snapdragon	
Argyranthemum sp. Marguerite	
Ballota nigra Black horehound	N
Betonica officinalis Betony	
Borago officinalis Borage	Med
Buddleia davidii Buddleia	
Buddleia davidii 'White profusion' Buddleia	
Buddleia globosa Orange ball tree	
Buddleia x weyeriana 'Golden Glow'	
Centaurea cyanus Cornflower	N
Centaurea nigra Knapweed	N
Centranthus ruber Red valerian	Med
Chaenomeles sp. Japanese quince	
Clematis montana 'Odorata' Clematis	
Cosmos sp. Cosmos	
Crocus sp. Crocus	
Dahlia sp. Dahlia	
Digitalis purpurea Foxglove	N
Echinops sp. Globe thistle	
Echium vulgare Viper's bugloss	N
Erica sp. Heath	
Eryngium maritimum Sea holly	N
Eryngium x giganteum	
Fritillaria meleagris Snake's head fritillary	N
Fuchsia sp. Fuchsia	
Galega officinalis Goat's rue	Med
Galeobdolon luteum Yellow archangel	N
Gaultheria sp. Gaultheria	
Geranium ibericum Geranium	Med
Geranium macrorrhizum Geranium	Med
Grevillea rosmarinifolia Grevillea	
Hieraceum sp. Hawkweed	N
Impatiens glandifera Bizzie Lizzie	
Ipomoea sp. Morning glory	
Jasminium sp. Jasmine	
Knautia arvensis Field scabious	N
Knautia macedonica 'Melton Pastels' Macedonian scabious	

Lamium alba White deadnettle	N
Lavendula sp. Lavender	Med
Limonium simulatum Statice	
Lotus corniculatus Bird'sfoot trefoil	N
Lycopersicon esculenta Tomato	
Mahonia x media Oregon grape	
Mahonia x media 'Winter Sun' Mahonia	
Meconopsis cambrica Welsh poppy	N
Monarda didyma Monarda, Bergamot	
Muscari sp. Grape hyacinth	
Nasturtium sp. Tropaeolum	
Nepeta cataria Catmint	N
Ornithogalum sp. Star of Bethlehem	
Penstemon sp. Penstemon	
Petunia sp. Petunia	
Phaseolus vulgaris French bean	
Pieris japonica Lily of the Valley bush	
Potentilla tabernaemontani Spring cinquefoil	N
Prunus persica Peach	
Pulicaria dysenterica Fleabane	N
Rehmannia elata Chinese foxglove	
Reseda lutea Wild Mignonette	N
Rhododendron sp. Rhododendron	
Rosmarinus officinalis Rosemary	Med
Rubus sp. Bramble	
Salvia patens 'Guanajuato' Salvia	
Salvia verticillata 'Purple Rain' Salvia	
Santolina sp. Santolina	
Senecio jacobaea Ragwort	N
Solidago virgaurea Goldenrod	
Stachys palustris Marsh woundwort	N
Succisa pratensis Devil's bit scabious	N
Symphytum officinale Comfrey	N
Tagetes patula French marigold	
Trifolium pratense Red clover	N
Trifolium repens White clover	N
Valeriana officinalis Common Valerian	N
Vicia sepium Bush vetch	N
Viola sp. Viola	
Vitex agnus-castus Chaste bush	
Zinnia sp. Zinnia	

Gardening for bumblebees -
late summer flowers

A riot of dahlia colours in a herbaceous border is bound to attract late summer bumblebees to visit. As perennials, dahlias are easy enough to cultivate and make a good colour splash into early autumn. One of the new varieties is shown above.

Cosmos (top left), in all its different colours, is guaranteed to attract bumblebees, even though the flowers sway around in windy weather on long stems. Policeman's Helmets (*Impatiens glandifera*) grows by rivers and is always a good nectar source (right). Petunias continue to be robbed in late summer, thistles enjoyed and statice is a good late flowerer; here a *B. pascuorum* collects orange pollen.

Fuchsia flower from late summer into autumn and are eagerly sought by bumblebees and honeybees.

A queen will often be seen foraging well into late winter on warm sunny days

Global warming

Bumblebee populations change with the weather. It is now thought that climate changes caused by global warming can effect the sorts of bumblebees you see. Not only do bumblebee populations fluctuate as a result, but extinctions and the introductions of new species happens. It has already started.

Two new bees are now present in Britain. First the impressive black carpenter bee, *Xylocopa violacea* (shown opposite) is now a regular visitor to the south of England having come over from France where it is common. It is not a bumblebee, but it is a very close relative and looks like one. It is a very distinctive species and easily spotted. The second example is another French insect, the Tree Bumblebee, *Bombus hypnorum* that has now been seen in various locations in southern England.

This movement of continental species northwards is a typical reaction for Mediterranean species expanding their range into areas that are now experiencing slightly warmer temperatures. At the same time those bumblebees that enjoy the kind of uniquely damp climate of Britain (known as the Atlantic climate) have to endure a slightly warmer temperature that they are not accustomed to. The result is that they die out if there is nowhere else cooler for them to go.

For instance if the species lives at the summit of a range of hills that has a special climate of its own, the summit would become too warm and there would be no-where else locally for the species to go. Therefore it becomes extinct. This is a major problem for many animals, not just bumblebees. So, as the hot and prolonged summers typical of a Continental style climate start to oust the wetter Atlantic climate then species have to make adaptations quickly, or die. As most wildlife cannot make adaptations relatively quickly they die.

There is clearly a limit to how hot a climate can become, since most of the bumblebees of the world live in the temperate zone, few in the tropics.

Likely effects of global warming

(not global cooling which is another matter, and possibility)

- New species to look out for
- Expansion and retraction of bumblebee ranges
- Familiar species likely to disappear
- Continued generations of some bumblebees each year
- Overwintering of colonies, not just queens

What you can do

- Plant Mediterranean plants such as *Monarda, Santolina, Salvias, Lavendula*.
- Look out for these interesting new carpenter bees from the Continent.

Although carpenter bees are not bumblebees they are closely related and fly with the general crowd of bumblebees and could easily be confused for bumblebees.

The three photographs shown here belong to the *Xylocopa* genus; the middle photograph shows one smothered in pollen. This is a relatively harmless carpenter bee that has distinctive violet reflective wings – that's where it gets its second name of *violacea*. It is much larger than a bumblebee, at about 6cm across with wings outstretched. The middle photograph is a male with two red antennal segments.

Characteristically its wings glint in the sunshine as it moves slowly between flowers, changing from violet, mauve and blue to black depending on the intensity of light and shade. It takes its time to visit a wide variety of colourful garden flowers, often resting for long periods, clearly wanting to be seen by potential predators. Having established its message of being seen and avoided, it flies on to investigate holes in brickwork, masonry, trellises and joinery wherever it can find a breeding chamber.

Xylocopa is common in Mediterranean Europe and is now a visitor to the Garden of England, Kent.

Hotter weather

The Chinese foxglove (*Rehmannia elata*) is a fabulous nectar source for bumblebees since it produces masses of flowers from spring until the first frosts. With bigger flowers than the usual foxglove (no relation other than in name) it is sought out by bumblebees. It grows as tall as *Digitalis* foxgloves and has lots of side branches with repeat flowering all season. When ordinary foxgloves have set seed, the Chinese foxglove continues well into autumn. The two species are illustrated together.

In hot summer borders it is not unusual to see the silvery spiky leaves of *Eryngium* x *giganteum*, here contrasted with the red flowers of *Penstemon*. They are both attractive to bumblebees. The heads of tiny flowers of the *Eryngium* are like magnets for bumblebees that probe them for nectar. In the wild these eryngiums or field eryngos live in excessively dry habitats such as limestone plateaus or coastal dunes and tolerate lots of heat.

Lavenders are essential for any garden to encourage bumblebees from summer through to late autumn. They are drought tolerant and do well when the weather is hot. Here a faded Buff-tailed Bumblebee, *Bombus* terrestris rests on top of the flowers.

The chaste tree, *Vitex agnus-castus*, is a robust shrub ideal for long hot summers, since it flowers well into late summer with tall spikes of flowers. As bumblebees need further nectar sources into the early autumn, this is a shrub that is worth cultivating.

Grevillea rosmarinifolia is a half-hardy or tender shrub or small tree from Australia that has red flowers that become smothered by bumblebees. It can also be grown in the conservatory, but be sure to let bumblebees in.

Rhododendron blossoms are big enough to dwarf bumblebees, but it does not stop the bumblebees foraging furiously for nectar. While bumbling about, the long arched stamens of the male part of the flower dust pollen onto the insect.

Operation Bumblebee was launched in 2005 by the company Syngenta (www.operationbumblebee.co.uk) to try to reverse the trend of bumblebees dying off in the countryside. A change in farm policy has seen a 97% reduction in grass and clover fields across the UK. Now Syngenta are planning to enlist 1000 farmers to plant an hectare each of special bumblebee wildflower mixture, to produce 1000 ha of new pollen and nectar habitat.

After a busy summer, all the bumblebees of a colony normally die off except for the queen that has mated, but with global warming some colonies may actually overwinter....

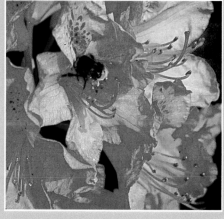

Vigorous 'pollen-shaking' has been seen in some bumblebees when they want to dislodge pollen from the flowers of rhododendron.

- they have an economic role in pollinating crops.

- they pollinate wildflowers in wayside, woodland and in the kitchen garden.

- they are part of insect biodiversity, with commitments to conserve them Europewide.

- they are in crisis – some species are contracting their ranges, becoming extinct in some areas, and overall their populations are falling, not only in the UK but on the Continent and in North America too.

- they have evolved a special relationship with certain flowers and both flower and insect would be lost if either disappears.

- they rarely hurt anyone.

- they are well-loved by most people.

- they are indicators of a healthy environment

Biodiversity Action Plan (BAP) Bumblebees

There are currently five bumblebee species that are on the UKs Biodiversity Action Plan (BAP) priority list; these plans aim to reverse the fortunes of various bumblebees:

Great Yellow Bumblebee	*Bombus distinguendus*
Carder Bumblebee	*Bombus humilis*
Large Garden Bumblebee	*Bombus ruderatus*
Short-haired Bumblebee	*Bombus subterraneus*
Shrill Carder Bee	*Bombus sylvarum*

BAP species are those that are experiencing population decline.

What you can do

- Find out what is in your neighbourhood, along verges, municipal gardens etc.
- Make bumblebee friendly places in the garden
- Record local data

Conservation

BAP species, the Shrill Carder Bee, *Bombus sylvarum* nectaring on Nasturtium (*Tropaeolum* sp.). Most bumblebees are well into hibernation in October, but late species, possibly encouraged by the effects of global warming continue to forage for nectar and pollen into November.

This bumblebee is in serious decline nationally in the UK. The Large Carder Bee, *Bombus muscorum*, is here collecting nectar from Morning Glory (*Ipomoea* sp.) in southern France. The species is identified by the foxy colour of its thorax.

The Brown-banded Carder-bee, *Bombus humilis*, visits the blue flowers of Viper's-bugloss, *Echium vulgare (above)*. This is a BAP species of bumblebee that is declining in south-east England. It was photographed in a key bumblebee stronghold, Dungeness, Kent, a protected area of shingle expanses. Viper's bugloss grows as a shrubby biennial and is tolerant to extreme conditions of wind and sun exposure in well drained soils. The plant is a major nectar source for bumblebees. Somewhat prickly it is worth growing in the garden since it attracts all sorts of insects.

Variable protection is afforded throughout Europe.

Village greens, verges and gardens

Clover has always been one of the favourite nectar sources for bumblebees, but long gone are the clover and lucerne fields that once adorned the countryside. Now bumblebees have to forage on field margins, roadside verges, village greens and in gardens. Bumblebees are now used commercially by vegetable growers in glasshouses and polytunnels, since they are readily available and can be brought in for pollination duty at short notice in the spring and summer. Tomatoes and pears now have improved fruit set when using bumblebees, especially in inclement weather. There are not enough bumblebees in the wild to go round.

Bumblebees provide a great service in town and country pollinating herbaceous plants, trees and shrubs. The images shown opposite show how the various plants have evolved ways and means to get the pollen onto the bumblebee whilst granting access to the nectaries. In the case of comfrey the long female parts actually touch the hairy body of the bumblebee (*B. pascuorum*) and collect pollen on the sticky ends of the apparatus (the stigma). Any pollen sticking to the hairs of the bumblebee will get onto the ripe stigmas and this will result in pollination. If the pollen comes from another plant of the same species this is cross-pollination.

Charles Darwin was always fascinated by bumblebees and studied them in his country garden in SE England in the mid-19th century. He was also interested in the actions of bumblebees (he called them 'humble-bees') in the pollination of members of the peas and beans family. These irregularly-shaped flowers have a sort of 'landing-stage' where the bees alight before crawling inside. Check out these flowers in the garden and notice how the reproductive parts of the flowers are placed so as to disperse or collect pollen from insect visitors.

Tongue length of bumblebees

The length of a bumblebee's tongue may play an important role in its ultimate survival, since tongue length is crucial for them in reaching nectaries. If long-tubed flowers disappear then long-tongued bumblebees may also disappear, though this does not account for *B. hortorum* or *B. pascuorum* (both with long tongues) which are widespread. The disappearance of crucial nectar sources may trigger local extinctions of bumblebees, and currently in the UK *B. monticola* and *B. soroeensis* have restricted ranges. However the situation is not that clear cut and what you can do as gardeners, is provide a good range of both long and short tubed flowers.

Long-tubed wildflowers to plant

Borage (*Borago officinalis*), Bird's foot trefoil (*Lotus corniculatus*), Black horehound (*Ballota nigra*), Marsh Woundwort (*Stachys palustris*), Red Clover (*Trifolium pratense*), White Dead-nettle, (*Lamium album*).

Short-tongued bumblebees: *B. hypnorum, jonellus, lucorum, monticola, pratorum, terrestris.*
Mid-tongued: *B. lapidarius, soroeensis*
Long-tongued: *B. distinguendus, hortorum, humilis, muscorum, pascuorum, ruderarius, ruderatus, sylvarum, subterraneus.*

There has been a 70% decline in some species of bumblebees in Britain since the 1970s.

Pollinating flowers

Red clover

Dahlia

Peach

Comfrey

Broad bean

Geranium

Sucking red clover flowers for the 'honey' is something that children and bumblebees share

Places to see bumblebees

The Eden Project in Cornwall is a great place to see bumblebees. They have free access to the domes and quite a number of species may be seen especially in the temperate and Mediterranean biome. With an abundance of flowers and a lack of adverse weather the bumblebees prosper inside these giant glasshouses. The floral displays outside with brightly coloured dahlias also extend the viewing season when bumblebees can be seen foraging up to mid November. At Eden there is also a giant bumblebee, which must be the largest imitation bumblebee in the world.

Another great place to see bumblebees is Wisley gardens in Surrey, just off the M25. This is the Royal Horticultural Society's showpiece garden where there are acres of colourful flower beds and borders. Bumblebees can often be seen jostling with the many different varieties of flowering plants, grown during an extended season from early spring to late autumn. It is always worth visiting municipal gardens as these are often honey-pots for bumblebees, even in city centres.

Bumblebees forage close to their nests, and usually within 400m

Places to see bumblebees

Bumblebee desert

Expanses of arable farmland are no use to bumblebees. In many places hedgerows have been removed, and waysides and woodland do not offer any nectar sources for bumblebees. These are bumblebee deserts.

Enhancement with tree and shrub planting along the edge of fields will encourage wildflowers to prosper. The needs of bumblebees are not best served by open agricultural fields, so all that can be done to plant up edges and strips will improve their lot. Bumblebees will benefit by suitable planting along green corridors.

It does seem ironic that urban sprawl is partly responsible for the decline of bumblebees through loss of greenfield and brownfield land, yet it is the best place for bumblebees when all the gardens are created.

There are up to 15-18 million private gardens (representing 270,000 ha) in Britain - great for biodiversity and for bumblebees

In your garden

Main locations to check out and to encourage bumblebees

Gardens are amongst the best places to see bumblebees. They breed and feed in ordinary gardens. If it were not for gardens, bumblebees would be in an even more serious decline.

Compost heaps are important nesting sites for bumblebees and they are also good places to place a bumblebee nest box.

Flowerbeds and borders offer both nectar and pollen sources for bumblebees.

Hedgerows are important places in the landscape for bumblebees since they have 'routes' through the garden that they regularly patrol, both inside and out of older hedgerows.

Kitchen gardens have a lot of peas and beans whose flowers provide nectar for bumblebees. Raspberries, blackberries and kiwi flowers also provide lots of inviting flowers.

Lawns and long tussocky grass have holes that bumblebees will use to make an underground nest or to use the moss and leaf litter to make hibernation areas.

Orchards with apple, plum, pear, peach and cherry all provide ample nectar and pollen for bumblebees.

Shrubberies that include species such as *Pieris*, tall ericas and *Gaultherias* become a hive of activity with bumblebees attracted in turn to the opening flowers.

Verges outside a house, if run a little wild, will provide wildflower nectar sources for bumblebees.

Trees with large trunks are used by bumblebees as 'buzzing spots', which is where bumbles scent-mark on their daily routes. A small glade of trees is also useful for bumblebees as sources of breeding sites in rough ground, and for the nectar from some tree flowers such as limes.

What you can do

- Grow French and Runner beans
- Keep a compost heap
- Keep a wood pile
- Plant spring nectar sources against a wall, such as Japanese quince (*Chanomeles*)
- Grow wildflowers such as annual French marigold (*Tagetes patula*), perennial Valerian, *Valeriana officinalis*).

In some regions more bumblebees are found in urban areas than in the countryside

Attracting bumblebees to the garden with window boxes, hanging baskets, trellises

Grow a mix of wild and garden plants to encourage bumblebees

Photographing Bumblebees

It's tricky and you do need good equipment and patience.

All the bumblebees in this book were photographed in the wild, which means trailing specimens to see where they go, second guessing their next move and having lucky breaks. Bumblebees are incredibly busy insects, working the flowers faster than honeybees, and only spending about 2-3 seconds at each flower. If you are very lucky the bumblebee will stop for a short break and will give you more than a few seconds to get the shot. At least they are generally consistent, working the same type of flower on their forays (except in the autumn) and so their movement between flowers is predictable.

Bumblebees never allow the luxury of tripods. They beat their wings at up to 200 times a second, so getting that depth of field shot with frozen wings is sometimes fraught. These images were mostly shot using a hand held Canon EOS 1Ds digital camera with a 105mm 1:2.8 macro lens and with a No. 1 58mm close up cap producing raw 30 megapixel images. All but half a dozen were shot in natural light which sets the scene so much better than with flash that produces a black background.

Once you have found a good nectar source for bumblebees, such as a clump of brambles, foxgloves, teasels, comfrey or deadnettles then it is worth waiting until the familiar black silhouette of a bumblebee flits between flowers, or the familiar buzz of a bumblebee announces its imminent arrival. Bumblebees work the flowers assiduously and it is then best to choose a flower that it is going to visit, choose the best angle for a good backdrop and pre-focus on the flower whilst waiting for the bumblebee to visit. You can hold the automatic focus down after the 'bleep' and take the shot, or make continuous shots the very second the bumblebee arrives. This predictive shooting will pay dividends.

The good thing about photographing bumblebees is that you can be out shooting them before breakfast and well after dinner in the evening, since they are early and late workers, compared to honeybees that are neatly tucked up in the hive at dawn and dusk.

There are many reasonably priced point and shoot digital cameras with optical zoom that take amazing close up photographs

The Buff-tailed Bumblebee in the UK has a buff tail, but on the continent, it is white

Studying bumblebees

These are 250 year old bumblebees, amongst the oldest in Europe, that Swedish naturalist, Carl Linneaus studied in the mid 18th century. There is no real need to kill bumblebees today, but they can be caught and inspected in observation tubes such as shown below, or checked for underneath paving slabs, or encouraged to visit bumblebee shelters.

An observation tube (right) with plunger is used to look at a bumble-bee for identification, or to mark it ready for release. It is about 9cm long.

The concrete slab (right) is 40cm square and is placed on the soil or on a lawn and it has a separate clear plastic sheet beneath. Periodically it can be lifted to reveal what has ventured beneath, such as hibernating bumblebees and other invertebrates.

The 'wildlife lodge' (10x12 x24cm) with cane entrance tube is typical of a number of proprietory bumblebee boxes that are readily available.

The French naturalist, Jean-Henri Fabre – a contemporary of Darwin – was also interested in bees

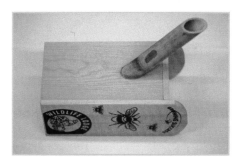

Bumblebee Habitats

Traditional bumblebee habitats are disappearing fast throughout Europe and this is why bumblebee populations are declining rapidly. Bumblebees are found in towns, village and open countryside, in fact just about anywhere with a healthy compliment of wildflowers, shrubs and trees. Sadly some parts of the countryside have now become bumblebee deserts since the waysides, woodlands and hedgerows and headlands have been ripped out and replaced with monocultures. This loss of wildflowers along field edges, ditches and hedgerows spelt the end of bumblebees in many parts of the countryside. Now more bumblebees may be found in urban areas than the countryside since they are attracted to variety of plants grown in gardens.

Why are bumblebees declining?

- Loss of nectar sources – fewer wildflowers
- Loss of verges – a 'cleaned up environment'
- Loss of habitat – no more hedgerows and flowery ditches
- Loss of pollen sources – fewer trees, shrubs and wildflowers
- Climate change – altering bumblebee population

Natural enemies of bumblebees

Both badgers and wax moth larvae destroy nests

Badgers are the main threat to bumblebees since they scratch out the underground nests and eat the honey and grubs. With their long hair protecting them, badgers are not troubled by the bumblebee stings. Look out for disrupted nests and a few bumblebees flying around in a disorientated fashion. Some birds eat bumblebees, particularly bee-eaters and butcher birds known for their habit of impaling bees, including bumblebees, on thorny trees, as a sort of living larder. These birds are mostly Mediterranean and rarely seen in the UK. On a much smaller scale, tiny mites (which are spiders) can be seen in small or large groups on bumblebees. These are parasites that do not seem to do the bumblebee any harm unless they reach large numbers. Internally, there are a number of parasites such as nematode worms that live within the body cavity of bumblebees and can cause some harm to them.

Equipment: Boxes etc

The author is not responsible for content on other websites.

www.alanecology.com	Alana Ecology Ltd.	t 01588 630173
www.ecotopia.co.uk	Ecotopia	
www.jacobijayne.co.uk	Jacobi Jayne	t. 0800 072 0130
www.nestbox.co.uk	Nestbox Company Ltd.	t. 0845 833 3133
www.watdon.co.uk	Watkins & Doncaster	
www.wildbird.org	Wildbird	
www.wildlifeservices.co.uk	Wildlife & Countryside Services	

Mail Order only

Envisage, The Old Brickyard, Kiln Lane, Swindon, SN2 2NP t. 01793 53 88 22.

Bumblebee boxes

Basic box with lid (above) internal view (below) showing feeder and kapok for nest materials.

It is fun to have a bumblebee box in the garden, to watch the comings and goings of bumblebees. You can entice them into their own home with diluted honey.

There are at least three different designs of bumblebee boxes, and many suppliers. This one is 36.5 x 22.5cm in weatherproof plastic with a lid that opens to reveal a view into the chambers through some tough perspex. The box has two chambers, a large (outer) one and a small (inner) one. The large one is the where the bumblebee will set up home, the inner one is where it will feed. There are two ventilation holes, one in each side. To attract bumblebees in the spring it is best to place the box away from direct sunlight, perhaps in the corner of a compost heap or next to a coloured garden object so that it can get a 'fix' as to where its home is. You can either paint a colour on the box, or place a piece of coloured plastic next to the box so that the bumblebees remember the way home.

habitat loss is the main overall threat to bumblebees in the countryside

Bumblebee names (cuckoos in bold)

Latin Name	Common Name	
Bombus campestris	**Field Cuckoo-bee**	
Bombus barbutellus	**Barbut's Cuckoo-bee**	
Bombus bohemicus	**Gypsy Cuckoo-bee**	
Bombus cullumanus	Cullen's Bumblebee	(extinct in early 1990s)
Bombus distinguendus	Great Yellow Bumblebee	(extinct in England & Wales)
Bombus hortorum	Garden Bumblebee	
Bombus humilis	Brown-banded Carder-bee	
Bombus hypnorum	Tree Bumblebee	
Bombus jonellus	Heath Bumblebee	
Bombus lapidarius	Red-tailed Bumblebee	
Bombus lucorum	White-tailed Bumblebee	
Bombus monticola	Mountain Humble-bee	
Bombus muscorum	Large or Moss Carder-bee	
Bombus pascuorum	Common Carder-bee	
Bombus pomorum	Apple Bumblebee	(extinct in Britain)
Bombus pratorum	Early Bumblebee	
Bombus ruderarius	Red-shanked Carder-bee	
Bombus ruderatus	Large Garden Bumblebee	
Bombus rupestris	**Hill Cuckoo-Bee**	
Bombus soroeensis	Broken-bellied Bumblebee	
Bombus subterraneus	Short-haired Bumblebee	
Bombus sylvarum	Shrill Carder Bumblebee	
Bombus sylvestris	**Forest Cuckoo-Bee**	
Bombus terrestris	Buff-tailed Bumblebee	
Bombus vestalis	**Vestal Cuckoo-Bee**	

A note on names

Common names have not yet been standardised. Some are very cumbersome, for instance the Garden Bumblebee is sometimes also called the Three-banded White-tailed Bumblebee. This list does not offer a solution, only a list of commonly used names. Latin names are still being argued about, for instance the similarities or differences of B. hortorum and B. ruderatus, as well as B. lucorum and B. magnus. - whether they should be separate species or not. Also, you may find B. monticola called B. lapponicus using an earlier name. This book does not go into the merits of each, so go to 'Further Information' for helpful identification books and read around the subject, or start to make some original observations yourself and contribute to the discussions.

Hurry - Bumblebees are becoming extinct in many areas of Europe & North America now

White deadnettle, *Lamium alba* offers a perfect fit for the Common Carder-bee

Glossary

BAP	Biodiversity Action Plan
Bee-fly	a bumblebee mimic, e.g. *Bombylius* sp.
biennial	a plant that flowers in its second year
bracts	parts of a flower that are sometimes colourful, e.g. clematis
Buzzing-spots	places where bumblebees buzz each year (different ones)
carder	refers to a bee that collects moss
carpenter bee	a large social bee that lays its egg in tunnels bored in wood, stems or artificial holes
cuckoo bumblebee	a bee that is parasitic inside bumblebee nests
drone	a male stingless bee
florets	part of a flower, not a petal, but often called ray florets
genus	a group of species with similar characters
hardy perennial	perennial that withstands hard frosts
herbaceous	plants that have soft rather than woody tissues
honey-pot	wax cup made by bumblebees for storing nectar
humble bee	an old English term for bumblebee
hymenoptera	the order of insects to which bees belong
mason bee	solitary bees of the *Osmia* genus that often live in holes in brickwork
mimic	an animal that copies another animal
nectary	a place where nectar is produced by a plant
parasite	an animal that lives on another animal without killing it
perennial	plants that come up year after year
Psithyrus	an old term for the genus of cuckoo bumblebees
robbing	the habit of bumblebees to get to the nectar by piercing petals
social bee	bees that have queens, workers and drones that live together
solitary bee	bees that do not live in communities
syrphid	hover-flies which is a group of true-flies
sp	shorthand for species
tabanid	a horsefly which is a group of true-flies
true-flies	flies belonging to the Order Diptera

Bumblebees fly in the Arctic, share habitat with polar bears and may forage for 24 hours
Bumblebees can fly at 0°C and keep their internal temperature at 30°C
The heart of a bumblebee beats about ten times a second.

Comfrey, *Symphytum officinale,* is a good nectar source for long-tongued bumblebees

Further Information

Books, Articles, CD-ROMs (OOP = Out of print)

Benton, T. 2000. *The Bumblebees of Essex*. Saffron Walden, Lopinga Books.

Benton, T. 2006. *Bumblebees*. London, Collins New Naturalists.

Buglife, 2005 Managing Priority Habitats for Invertebrates. 2nd edition. CD-ROM

Edwards, M. & Jenner, M. *Field Guide to the Bumblebees of Great Britain and Ireland*. Countryside & Garden Conservation series. Ocelli Ltd. Excellent for identification

Edwards, M. & Williams, P., 2004. Where have all the bumblebees gone, and could they every return? *British Wildlife*. June 2004. pp. 305-312.

English Nature, 2005. *Help save the Bumblebee*. Peterborough. two free leaflets

Free, J.B. 1982. *Bees and Mankind*. London, G. Allen & Unwin. Chapter 2 on Bumblebees (pp.15-35) OOP, but important work.

Free, J. & Butler, C. 1959. *Bumblebees*. London, New Naturalist. OOP, classic work

Heinrich, B. 2004. *Bumblebee Economics*. Harvard University Press (paperback)

Goulson, D. 2003. *Bumblebees, ecology and behaviour*. Oxford University Press.

Howes, F.N. 1979. *Plants and Beekeeping*. London, Faber. OOP. for nectar sources

O'Toole, C. 2002. *Bumblebees*. Rothley, Osmia Publications.

Prŷs-Jones, O. & Corbet, S. 1987. *Bumblebees*. Naturalist's Handbook No 6. OOP

Sladen, F., 1912. *The Humblebee*, Facsimile Edition, 1989. Logaston Press. OOP

Stubbs, A. & Falk, S.J. 2002. *British Hoverflies*. Brit. Ent. & Nat. Hist. Soc. for mimics

Websites

www.buglife.org.uk — general information and status of bumblebees

www.bumblebee.org — a personal view of bumblebees

www.caithness.org/nature/bees/guide.htm — identification of Highland bumblebees

www.english-nature.org.uk/news/story.asp?ID=466 — plight of the bumblebee

www.hymenoptera.de — general remarks on bumblebees (in English & German)

www.lbp.org.uk/03action_pages/ac27_bumble.html — action plan for *B. humilis*

www.nhm.ac.uk/entomology/bombus/decline.html — on distribution and decline

www.searchnbn.net — distribution maps of UK bumblebees

www.rhs.org.uk/advice/profiles1200/wildflower_meadow.asp — wildflower meadows

Societies, Newsletters (N)

www.amentsoc.org/ — Amateur Entomologist's Society

www.benhs.org.uk — British Journal of Entomology and Natural History

www.buglife.org.uk — Buglife - The Invertebrate Conservation Trust (N)

www.bwars.com — BWARS - Bees Wasps and Ants Recording Society (N)

Bumblebee & wildflower mixes

www.naturalsurroundings.org.uk

www.naturescape.co.uk

www.nickys-nursery.co.uk

www.wildseeds.co.uk

The author is not responsible for content on other websites.

Buglife - The Invertebrate Conservation Trust is the first organisation in Europe devoted to the conservation of all invertebrates, and is actively engaged in saving Britain's rarest bugs, slugs, snails, bees, wasps, ants, beetles and many more fascinating invertebrates